BRITAIN IN PICTURES

THE BRITISH PEOPLE IN PICTURES

—————

INSECT LIFE IN BRITAIN

GENERAL EDITOR
W. J. TURNER

The Editor is most grateful to all those who have
so kindly helped in the selection of illustrations
especially to officials of the various public
Museums Libraries and Galleries and
to all others who have generously
allowed pictures and MSS
to be reproduced

INSECT LIFE
IN
BRITAIN

GEOFFREY TAYLOR

WITH
8 PLATES IN COLOUR
AND
22 ILLUSTRATIONS IN
BLACK & WHITE

COLLINS · 14 ST. JAMES'S PLACE · LONDON
MCMXXXXV

PRODUCED BY
ADPRINT LIMITED LONDON

PRINTED IN GREAT BRITAIN AT
THE SUN ENGRAVING CO LTD LONDON AND WATFORD
ON MELLOTEX BOOK PAPER MADE
BY TULLIS RUSSELL & CO LTD MARKINCH SCOTLAND

LIST OF ILLUSTRATIONS

PLATES IN COLOUR

,BLACK AND WHITE ILLUSTRATIONS

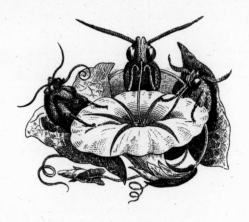

Butterfly, Mayfly, Bumblebee, and Moth
Living their year, their month, their days, their hours
(But this illusion, Time, may be a cloth
Cut each to his own measure) among flowers
Where some make love, and some make wax or honey,
No species hindering its own kind's affairs;
Whilst men make what? Make war on men, make money
(Yet while they prey, in fairness add, make prayers).

"The proper study of mankind is Man."
True—tooth and nail. But though we still have hopes,
Hadn't the Psalmist's son a rune that ran
In not too flattering complement to Pope's?
A rule it may seem silly to despise—
"Consider thou the Ant's ways and be wise."

INSECTS AND ENGLISH ENTOMOLOGY

"TEN thousand forms! ten thousand different tribes!"—James Thomson, the author of *The Seasons*, and a good naturalist, was guilty of an under-estimate; for entomologists now recognise more than twelve thousand species of British insects, each with its own intrinsic interest and importance, and—what is more to the point—each one of which must be labelled with at least two Latin words—so that a bare list of them would nearly double the space allotted for my text. Besides, there is nothing distinctive about any particular English insect. From mere inspection it might, for all it seems, for all it knows or cares, perhaps, be French or Dutch—might even

7

be so by birth if it happens to be one of our frequent immigrants. Further, a glance at the British Museum Library catalogue leads one to suppose that there may already be more books on insects than there are species. My problem, therefore, is different from W. J. Turner's on *English Music*, or John Betjeman's on *English Small Towns*. The problem would be made even more complex if we had to go back in time, for English insects are members of our oldest families, tracing a descent from the period of our most ancient fossil-bearing rocks—the limestone-slate strata of the so-called Silurian era. Incidentally they do not seem to have made much progress since the day they were made—wherein they differ little from ourselves, who are aristocrats of a more recent creation.

But first, what *is* an insect—of any age or nationality? Thomson, writing in the early eighteenth century, would certainly have included spiders, wood-lice, and centipedes—creatures which scientists have, since the time of the English zoologist Thomas Pennant, placed in other departments of the great group of animals known as Arthropoda or Articulata—the group which also includes the true insects or Hexapoda. As the name Hexapoda implies, insects have six legs; and anyone can recognise a perfect, fully developed, insect, distinguishing it from any animal such as a spider with which it could conceivably be confused, by merely counting its legs. A mature insect may or may not have wings—most of them do—but it always has six legs. The typical insect also passes through a series of well-defined changes, hatching from the egg as a grub or caterpillar (known as a "larva"), transforming itself from active grub or caterpillar into a generally inert pupa or chrysalis, hatching again from the chrysalis as a perfect insect which will, having found its mate, start the cycle going once more.

Proper appreciation of this insect embryology is comparatively recent. Our remoter forefathers supposed that insects were spontaneously generated from all sorts of decaying organic matter. The Biblical text "Out of the strong came forth sweetness" is an evident example of this, and even Isaac Walton seems to have accepted something of the sort from Pliny and Du Bartas. In fact, it was not till the late seventeenth century that such ideas were finally discredited—partly as a result of the researches and the observations of the first great English naturalist, John Ray. Ray, who was born in 1627 and died in 1705, began by being a botanist, but on the death of his friend, Francis Willughby, he took to zoology, and from 1690 onwards he gave up nearly all his time to the study of insects. Ray's work gave an enormous impetus to Entomology, and during the eighteenth century insects—particularly English insects, began to come into their own. Martin Lister and the great John Hunter among the true scientists, popularisers like Goldsmith, serious naturalists like Benjamin Stillingfleet and White of Selborne, poets such as Thomson and Erasmus Darwin, all contributed to insect popularity, till, in the nineteenth century popularity became enthusiasm. The way to this was prepared, round the turn of the century, by a group of

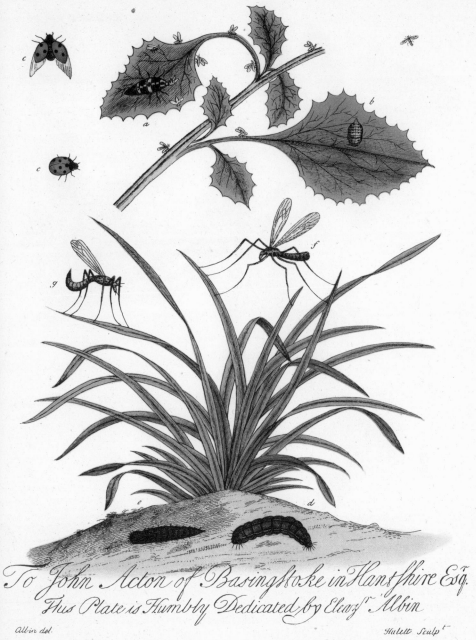

To John Acton of Basingstoke in Hantshire Esq.
This Plate is Humbly Dedicated by Eleazr Albin

Albin del.   Hulett Sculpt

LADYBIRD AND DADDY-LONG-LEGS: *COCCINELLA* AND *TIPULA OLERACEA*
Coloured engraving by Eleazar Albin from his *Natural History of English Insects*, 1720

SILVER STRIPE HAWK MOTH: *SPHINX CELERIO*
Coloured engraving by E. Donovan from his *Natural History of British Insects*, 1797

ardent entomologists, Edward Donovan, Thomas Marsham, and that great collector Dru Drury. Drury was a silversmith in the Strand by profession, but he was an insect-hunter by passionate inclination. Intermittent bankruptcy did not deter him from spending considerable sums on his hobby. Nor did he confine himself to English insects. Whenever he heard of a ship sailing from an English port to Africa, Asia, or America, he scraped acquaintance with one of her officers and persuaded him to collect for him in distant lands. He published the results in magnificent quarto volumes, and on his death in 1803 left a monumental collection which was sold, in separate lots, for about a thousand pounds—far less than he had spent in gathering it. In 1833 the Entomological Society was founded by Edward Bevan and others, but the two men to whom English entomology perhaps owes more than to anyone else were the long-lived William Kirby and his friend and collaborator William Spence. The Rev. William Kirby, Rector of Barnham, F.R.S., an original member of the Linnean Society, was born in 1759 and died, with all his entomological faculties about him, in 1850. He began to correspond with Spence, a man some twenty-five years his junior and who outlived him by ten years, in 1805, and their names are now linked as are those of Liddell and Scott or Beaumont and Fletcher. Kirby and Spence's *Introduction to Entomology; or Elements of the Natural History of Insects: comprising an Account of Noxious and Useful Insects, of their Metamorphoses, Food, Stratagems, Habitations, Societies, Motions, Noises, Hybernation, Instinct, etc., etc.*, to give it, as it deserves, its full title, was the classic guide throughout the Victorian era. During that era, under the stimulus of such excellent writers as P. H. Gosse, James Rennie, and Frank Buckland, and of the artist, John Curtis, natural history in all its branches became the rage among the leisured classes and even among the officers of Her Majesty's army. Schoolboys collected butterflies as never before, and aquariums of miscellaneous fish and aquatic insects formed part of the common furnishings of fashionable boudoirs. For women were no less ardent than men and boys. Margaret Emily Shore was watching Mason wasps at the age of fifteen and writing of them in her Journal. An acute entomologist was lost when she died at twenty, in 1829. Mary Delabeche Dillwyn, afterwards Mrs. Nicholl, lived to a more normal entomological age—as typified by such men as Kirby and Fabre—hunted insects round the world from the Balkans to Brazil, and formed the largest private collection of butterflies of her time. Such was the prestige of natural science in that day—she died in 1922 aged 83—that she was not even considered markedly eccentric. The publication of Charles Darwin's bomb-shell, *The Origin of Species*, near the middle of the century, merely raised pre-existing sentiment and interest to fever-pitch. Fossils, flowers, and insects gave point to the sermon and adorned the novel. With growing industrialism and the consequent urbanisation, country pursuits began to take on their present nostalgic tinge. All this was good for entomology.

Unfortunately—no matter how unscientific it may sound, one cannot regret one's regrets—facts and theories accumulated so fast during the period that the age of the great amateur naturalists, of whom Darwin was certainly among the greatest, and for all of whom the study of insects formed a major interest, may be said to have closed with that remarkable observer the Rev. J. G. Wood, whose books must have aroused many a childish curiosity besides my own. I call Wood the last of the great amateurs because, though he was born in 1827 and died as long ago as 1889, some of his vast number of books, many of which were expressly written for the young, remained in print well into the present century, and, for all I know, may still be in print —they should be, for such a book as *Homes Without Hands* is both readable and informative. But, so great was the growth of the natural sciences and of the science of entomology amongst them, that they became indigestible in bulk. Country clergymen, though they might still hope to make occasional significant contributions—as indeed they still may and do—could not, among their other duties, keep up with the flowing tide of research. Specialisation was the only way out, and by the time I myself, after the last war, became a professional entomologist, I was compelled to confine my studies almost entirely to two closely allied species of dipterous fly. Not that *Hypoderma bovis* and *Hypoderma lineatum* are not most interesting insects; but after concentration on them for two years, after counting, with the aid of a microscope, the larval spines on an inexhaustible number of specimens, and after embodying my conclusions in contributions to learned journals which no one but other specialists would ever read, I could not see those flies as a lifetime's preoccupation, and I am not sorry that fate should have parted me from them.

None the less, perhaps one's regrets at the passing of what seems a more leisurely, spacious age are ill-conceived. The rigorous scientist and the mere nature-lover have largely parted company it is true, but Nature, neither more nor less, is still there to be looked at, loved, partially understood, and, if you like, worshipped. Nor is the lover of nature ever likely to be confronted with all the twelve thousand British species. Such insects as he comes across or seeks out he may observe as the old naturalists observed them—worthy men like the amiable Benjamin Stillingfleet of whom Thomas Pennant said that "he attempted to destroy the false shame that attended the devotee to Ornithology, the chase of the Insect, the search after the Cockle, or the poring over the Grass." And if he has the not uncommon acquisitive instinct, like that seventeenth-century Lady Glanville who was thought mad for gathering insects and in whose posthumous defence Ray had to appear as a witness for her sanity in a trial at Exeter, he may, and now with no lunatic imputations, become a collector. For observation, nothing is required but patience, a pocket lens, and a tendency to explore every avenue and to leave no stone unturned. For collecting, he will need a little simple paraphernalia. Here is Spence's account of "the little parade of apparatus" with which the

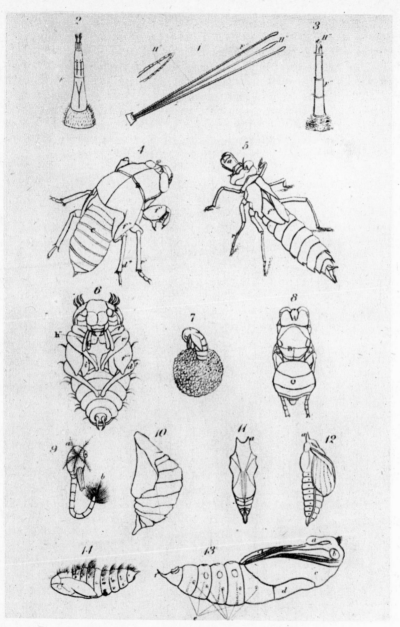

OVIPOSITORS AND PUPAE OF VARIOUS INSECTS
Line engraving from Kirby and Spence's *Introduction to Entomology*, 1826

11

Rev. William Kirby's "extensive and valuable acquisitions were made" :—

"If going to any distance, he would put into his pocket a forceps-net and small water-net, with which to catch bees, flies, and aquatic insects; but in general, I do not remember to have seen ,him use a net of any description. His numerous captures of rare and new Coleoptera were mostly made by careful searching for them in their haunts, from which—if trees, shrubs, or long grass, etc.—he would beat them with his walking-stick into a newspaper, and in this way, he would bring home in a few small phials in his waistcoat pockets, and in a moderate-sized collecting box, after an afternoon's excursion, a booty often much richer than his companions had secured with their more elaborate apparatus."

Mr. Kirby's pockets were, no doubt, cut on a generous pattern; his simple apparatus was probably yet more complex than that of Crabbe's entomological "friend the Weaver," who will be remembered by all readers of *The Borough*. The collector will also need a certain amount of elementary technical skill in dealing with his insects once he has collected them. In this respect we hav· certainly made some minor improvements on the eighteenth century amateurs. Dru Drury, that indefatigable searcher after specimens, has the following paragraph in his pamphlet, printed about 1768 and entitled *Directions for Collecting Insects*:—

"It is necessary to mention that butterflies should not, like other insects, be held to the fire to be killed, because the fire will crimple and shrivel up their wings and spoil them; neither should they be thrown into hot water, a pinch with the finger and thumb will be sufficient to kill them."

In spite of the implications—indeed, the specific directions—as to the treatment of insects other than butterflies, Drury's pamphlet ends with this financial encouragement :—

"Whatever quantity is collected (either little or great) is desired to be brought to Mr. Drury, at the corner of Love Lane, in Wood Street, near Cheapside, who will give sixpence a piece for them, either large or small."

No wonder the man went bankrupt. Nowadays one cannot too strongly recommend the use of the ordinary cyanide "killing-jar"—the "stink-pot" of one's school days—or, at the least, bruised laurel leaves in the bottom of a well-corked bottle. Another of Drury's instructions is to be frowned upon—that of impaling living insects on pins, so that they will stay put when they are captured. I do not know that this practice is particularly cruel—judging by the way a wasp whose head and thorax, having been parted from its abdomen by the breakfast knife, will continue greedily to consume marmalade, it is probably not cruel; insects in general seem singularly insensitive to pain—but such impaling may lead to serious damage, and ought not to be necessary.

For the rest, the collector will find instructions as to setting, mounting, naming, and displaying his specimens in many excellent "Handbooks to Our Common Insects" with which this discursive essay is by no means in competition.

INSECTS AND THE ENGLISH SEASONS

AFRICAN insects, Brazilian insects, even South European insects, are not dependent on the seasons, are not subject to the climate, to any thing like the extent that the insects of these islands are. Our own unpredictable climate, our weather in fact, which forms our staple conversational gambit and the stock centre of our complaints, has really added enormously to the excitement of our living, and particularly to our appreciation of Nature—above all in the fields of botany and entomology. We know that spring has come by the primrose, but hardly less by the primrose-coloured Brimstone butterfly.

The Brimstone, or the, in most places, much commoner Small Tortoiseshell is likely to be one's first butterfly of the year. Either may be seen on sunny days in March, and these two species are probably the longest lived of all our native butterflies. Gilbert White—inevitably one refers to that paragon among field-naturalists—gives February 13th, St. Valentine's Eve, which is appropriate enough, as the date of the Brimstone's earliest appearance; but in another year he did not notice one before April 2nd. I myself have never seen it, in Wiltshire, earlier than the first week in March. Normally it disappears before the end of June, though William Markwick gives the latest date for it as December 24th. But this must have been a freak specimen, since the Brimstone has only one breeding season. In this it differs from the Small Tortoiseshell, of which there are two broods in the year—one in June and the other as late as September—so that Tortoiseshells are common insects from early spring till late autumn. Indeed a bright day in the depth of winter will often bring one of them fluttering to the window-pane from the corners and crevices of our houses, where many of them spend the winter months.

With the progress of spring more and more species of butterflies—and, of course, not only of butterflies—put in their appearance. Orange-tips, Cabbage Whites, rarities such as the Glanville Fritillary (so named by the eighteenth-century entomologist Moses Harris—I hope after the Lady Glanville who collected insects so "madly") which lives chiefly in the Isle of Wight, immigrants like the fairly common Painted Lady which occasionally does breed in these Islands, but numbers of which also migrate hither from, perhaps, as far away as North Africa, these and many more will be on the wing before May is out. Our climate however plays odd tricks. A few years ago, in the part of the country where I happened to be staying, it began to snow on the afternoon of May 10th. Without freezing it continued to snow hard for most of the night, until next morning in brilliant sunshine the garden appeared under more than six inches of snow with tulips and other flowers projecting through it. The effect was like an iced birthday cake sprinkled with those microscopic many-coloured sweets that we used to call "hundreds-and-thousands." After breakfast the butterflies began to appear—a pair of Orange-tips, a White looking very off-white, and a Tortoiseshell or two—and the scene was what the old naturalists would have described as in the highest degree curious. Fortunately for the butterfly population of the district, the snow had all melted by the end of the day.

Butterflies are beautiful but, comparatively speaking, they are not as a rule of what one might call outstanding interest. None the less, perhaps the most exciting of all our native insects is the rare Large Blue, *Maculinea arion* (or, in some books, *Polyommatus arion*, a certain uncertainty as to names is one of the troubles about insects), which has been found in Wiltshire and in North Wales, but which is now practically confined to parts of Cornwall and the Cotswolds. This Large Blue butterfly lays its eggs singly on the buds of wild thyme on which the pinkish caterpillar begins to feed as soon as it hatches. When it has grown a bit and changed its skin about three times, it gets restless and begins to wander round. Hummocks on which wild thyme grows are often nests of the small red ant, *Myrmica rubra*, and the caterpillar wanders until it finds, or is found by, one of these red ants. The ant begins to caress the caterpillar which, under the stimulus of her attentions, exudes, from a gland in its tenth segment, a sweet liquid. This liquid the ant drinks, repeating the caressing operation at intervals. After this sort of thing has been going on for, perhaps, an hour, the caterpillar suddenly hunches up the front part of its back, the ant seizes it in its jaws as a cat might pick up a kitten, and carries it off into the ants'-nest. There, safely under ground, the ants feed it on undersized specimens of their own young, milking its sweet fluid from it in return. For six weeks it feeds on ant-larvæ, growing to three times its size, and through the winter it hibernates in a special cavity in the nest. Next spring it wakes up and is again fed on ant-larvæ until it turns into a chrysalis. It remains in the chrysalis state for some three weeks, hatches out as a perfect butterfly, creeps through the passages of the ants'-nest into

LARGE BLUE BUTTERFLY: *Maculinea Arion*, f.
Pencil drawing by Vere Temple

the open air, climbs a blade of grass, and unfolds its wings. This quite astonishing story has only fairly recently been observed and confirmed by Dr. Chapman and Mr. Frohawk. Well may one ask by what conceivable natural "evolutionary" process, Lamarkian, Darwinian, or De Vriesian, can such a complex, eccentric, aberrant adaptation have been brought about.

The caterpillar of the Large Blue is not the only insect that ants have more or less domesticated for the sake of "milk." The Black Garden Ant, *Lasius niger*, will milk honey-dew from the Aphids or Green-fly that infest roses and other cultivated plants, keeping special herds of them for this purpose. The ant will first stroke the Aphis with her feelers and then suck the two

15

little tubular teats that project from its hind quarters. Aphids are in themselves, and apart from their utility to ants and their inutility to gardeners, of some interest in as much as they are among the not very large number of insects that, on occasion, reproduce their kind parthenogenetically—that is to say, by virgin birth. It is strictly a virgin *birth*, because the young of these generations are brought forth alive, not hatched from eggs. Virgin births, giving rise to one female brood after another, are the rule from spring to autumn. But towards the end of the season males and females are born. These mate and the females lay eggs which last through the winter, hatching out in the spring as the first of the following year's virgin mothers.

The great enemy of the Green-fly, and, therefore, a friend to the gardener, though presumably counted a pest among the ants, is the Ladybird—one of our early spring beetles, as both Thomas Gray and Gilbert White have recorded, the Ladybird, or Lady-cow, Barnaby bug, Cush-cow Lady, and Our Lady's Cow, as it is called in some parts of the country, is both important, in that its odd-looking larvæ feed lavishly on the Green-fly, and also of some extrinsic interest because of its folk-lore connections.

Everyone knows the nursery rhyme :

> Ladybird, ladybird fly away home,
> Thy house is on fire, thy children will roam,
> All except Nan who sits on her pan
> Weaving gold laces as fast as she can—

or one of its many variants (that one came from Lancashire). One of the Brontës (not Emily, it seems) wrote a more poetic version :

> Ladybird ! Ladybird ! fly away home,
> Night is approaching, and sunset is come;
> The herons are flown to their trees by the Hall;
> Felt, but unseen, the damp dewdrops fall.
> This is the close of a still summer day;
> Ladybird ! Ladybird ! haste ! fly away !

Well, anyhow that nursery rhyme is said to be both ubiquitous and exceedingly ancient—prehistoric, in fact. And learned folklorists and students of comparative religion have traced our humble Ladybird back to the august company not only of Icarus, but also of the Egyptian Gods. To the admiring amateur such scholarly speculation seems not more improbable than most. Like the Painted Lady butterfly and other of our insects, the English Ladybirds are joined in some seasons by large numbers of migrants from France and southern Europe where they feed on the Green-fly of the orange orchards—a fact which, by way of oranges, may have helped their association with a Sun Myth.

Ladybirds, or at least their larvæ, have brought us into the full blaze of our temperate summer.

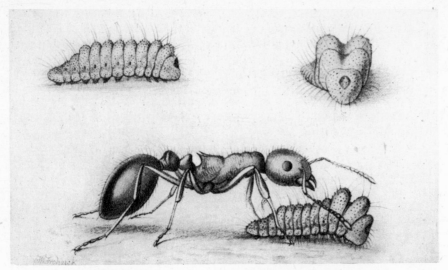

ANT, *Myrmica Laevimodis*, MILKING THE LARVA OF A BUTTERFLY, *Lycaena Arion*
Drawing by J. W. Frohawk, 1915

To the majority of people I suppose that the most noticed if not the most notable of summer insects are the flies—mere flies without prefix; that is members of the great tribe of *Diptera*. They have, indeed, their occasional fore-names, as House flies, Horse flies, Gad flies, and so on. Izaak Walton enumerates some of them :

"Now for Flies, which is the third bait wherewith trouts are usually taken. You are to know, that there are so many sorts of flies as there be of fruits : I will name you but some of them; as the dun-fly, the stone-fly, the red-fly, the moor-fly, the tawny-fly, the shell-fly, the cloudy- or blackish-fly, the flag-fly, the vine-fly; there be of flies, caterpillars, and canker-flies, and bear-flies; and, indeed, too many either for me to name, or for you to remember. And their breeding is so various and wonderful, that I might easily amaze myself, and tire you in a relation of them."

Heaven knows to what species or genera entomologists would fit some of Walton's names, but I think by "canker-flies" he means chrysalids, and by "bear-flies" he may mean the "woolly-bear" caterpillars of the Tiger moth. I have no idea what the shell-fly may be, nor the cloudy- or blackish-fly. However, what so excellent an artist as Izaak Walton feared to do in the way of tiring his reader it would ill become a lesser writer to run the risk of. But, as he said, the breeding of flies is certainly various and wonderful. The Swedish naturalist Linnæus said that three flies would consume the carcase of a horse as quickly as a lion could. He referred, of course, to the maggots which hatch from the flies' eggs. A single fly will lay over a hundred eggs.

17

These will be maggots in less than a fortnight, and in another ten days a new generation of female flies will be laying their centuries of eggs. It has been calculated—I have not checked the calculation—that if these flies themselves remained unchecked the offspring of a single mother would, in one season, number more than five and a half million. It is an unpleasant thought for a glorious summer day.

Naturally, though, flies do not remain unchecked. Birds and beasts and other insects, and even some plants, prey on them; and man is their constant enemy. But:

> Chief to heedless flies the window proves
> A constant death; where, gloomily retir'd,
> The villain spider lives, cunning, and fierce.
> Mixture abhorr'd ! Amid a mangled heap
> Of carcases, in eager watch he sits,
> O'erlooking all his waving snares around.

And James Thomson was pretty well right. If you leave plenty of spider-webs about your house you will have fewer flies—I have tried it; but to most housewives it will seem a desperate expedient, and fortunately there are less untidy ways of reducing the number of house flies. Cleanliness is the great thing, and branches of the common Elder are both decorative and effective. But let us move on. The prolific *Muscidæ* are not the only summer insects, and having turned up Thomson, one is encouraged to quote him again :

> Through the greenwood glade,
> Some love to stray; there lodg'd, amus'd and fed,
> In the fresh leaf. Luxurious, others make
> The meads their choice, and visit every flower.

The relationship between flowers and insects is one of the most attractive of natural history studies. There can be no doubt that flowers as we see them were primarily invented for insects, and only secondarily, perhaps, for our delight. They are the sexual organs of those vegetables that bear them, and insects are the means of consummating the "Loves of the Plants," on which Erasmus Darwin wrote his once famous, now unduly neglected, poem. The relationship between animal and vegetable is often curiously complex, as Erasmus's grandson, Charles Darwin, has shown in particular instances. Consider what that great and patient observer has to say about the intricate links on which may depend the seed-setting of two plants :

"I find from experiments," he writes, "that humble-bees are almost indispensable to the fertilisation of the heartsease (*Viola tricolor*), for other bees do not visit this flower. I have also found that the visits of these bees are necessary for the fertilisation of some kinds of clover. Humble-bees alone visit red clover, as other bees cannot reach the nectar. Hence we may

BLUEBOTTLE : *Musca Chloris*
Detail from a coloured engraving by John Curtis from his *British Entomology*, 1835

infer as highly probable that, if the whole genus of humble-bees become extinct or very rare in England, the heartsease and red clover would become very rare, or wholly disappear. The number of humble-bees in any district depends in a great measure upon the number of field-mice, which destroy their combs and nests; and Colonel Newman, who has long attended to the habits of humble-bees, believes that more than two-thirds of them are thus destroyed all over England. Now the number of mice is largely dependent, as everyone knows, on the number of cats; and Colonel Newman says,

'Near villages and small towns I have found the nests of humble-bees more numerous than elsewhere, which I attribute to the number of cats that destroy the mice.' Hence it is quite credible that the presence of a feline animal in large numbers in a district might determine, through the intervention first of mice then of bees, the frequency of certain flowers in that district !''

If there were no other reason for encouraging that feline animal, heartsease and clover would provide one. The adaptation—in many cases the fantastically elaborate adaptation—of flowers to their insect visitors is a matter for the most curious admiration. Charles Darwin himself wrote one of his most enthralling books on the *Fertilisation of Orchids*, paying particular attention to the British genera and species. Enthralling it certainly is— any book about the beautiful and rather sinister orchid family would be—yet I must be careful not to inflate my language, else what word shall I apply to another book of Darwin's, on *Insectivorous Plants* ? Though plants have been provided with flowers in all their different shapes and colours and various flavours of nectar for no other reason, apparently, than to secure cross-pollination by insects, yet it is a commonplace that the relationship between plants and insects is not always a friendly one. There is, for instance, the Cuckoo-pint or Lords-and-Ladies (*Arum maculatum*) which, because its anthers produce pollen before its stigmas are ready to receive it, imprisons, much against

SPARKLER OR TIGER BEETLE: *Cicindela Campestris*
Coloured engraving by E. Donovan from his
Natural History of British Insects, 1813

their will, large numbers of small flies in its lobster-pot of a spathe until such time as they have brought about the desired consummation, and then releases them. That is mere false imprisonment. On the other hand, the depredations of insects are notorious— they frequently go as far as murder. But, as the title of Darwin's book implies, this killing business is not quite one-sided. The Butterworts, the Bladderworts, and the Sundews (to mention only English plants) hit back in a passive sort of way, attracting small insects to their leaves only to consume them.

Darwin begins his book with a beguiling directness, like one of our older novelists:

CATERPILLAR AND CHRYSALIS OF PUSS MOTH
Phalaena Vinula. Detail from a coloured
engraving by E. Donovan, 1794

"During the summer of 1860, I was surprised by finding how large a number of insects were caught by the leaves of the common sun-dew (*Drosera rotundifolia*) on a heath in Sussex. I had heard that insects were thus caught, but knew nothing further of the subject. I gathered by chance a dozen plants, bearing fifty-six fully expanded leaves, and on thirty-one of these dead insects or remnants of them adhered. . . . On one plant all six leaves had caught their prey; and on several plants very many leaves had caught more than a single insect. On one large leaf I found the remains of thirteen distinct insects. Flies (*Diptera*) are captured much oftener than other insects. The largest kind which I have seen caught was a small butterfly (*Cænonympha pamphilus*); but the Rev. H. M. Wilkinson informs me that he found a large living dragon-fly with its body firmly held by two leaves."

Thus Darwin in his fifty-second year sets out on a new study, and he pursues it cautiously but relentlessly, and never—or hardly ever—dully (some of the chemical experiments can be skipped) for three hundred and seventy pages.

I have never seen Sun-dews or Butterworts catch anything as big as a dragon-fly. One regrets that dragonfly, for he himself was a voracious enemy of gnats and midges and must merely have come to rest on the Sun-dew from his altogether useful labours.

Charles Darwin was a scientific naturalist who, as he says himself, lost all interest in poetry. Robert Bloomfield was a shoemaker-naturalist and a poet, and after reading Darwin for an hour or so—as one does if one begins to read him at all—it is a relief to turn to a poet-entomologist and find :

> Just where the parting bough's light shadows play,
> Scarce in the shade, nor in the scorching day,
> Stretched on the turf he lies, a peopled bed,
> Where swarming insects creep around his head.
> The small dust-colour'd beetle climbs with pain,
> O'er the smooth plantain-leaf, a spacious plain !
> Thence higher still, by countless steps convey'd,
> He gains the summit of a shiv'ring blade,
> And flirts his filmy wings, and looks around,
> Exulting in his distance from the ground.
> The tender speckled moth here dancing seen,
> The vaulting grasshopper of glossy green,
> And all prolific Summer's sporting train,
> Their little lives by various powers sustain.

With that charming entomological vignette of a peaceful Suffolk day in 1798, when other parts of the Kingdom were suffering our last foreign invasion, we may as well pass from summer into autumn—a season of mists, no doubt, and of mellow fruitfulness; but also of wasps within the mellow fruit.

Few people think well of wasps, and I have known virtuous and courageous men, clergymen and soldiers, who were exasperated and frightened at their approach. It is true that wasps eat our ripe fruit, that they get into the jam, and that their stings can cause discomfort. Yet no wasp ever stung for the mere fun of it, and in general, the good they do far outweighs the bad. For wasps, both the solitary and the more noticeable social sorts, feed their numerous grubs almost entirely on caterpillars—for which the gardener, the fruit-grower, and even the parson and the soldier, should bless them. The small Mason Wasp, for instance, which may be watched constructing its towered burrows on a dry bank, fills each of its three or four cells with as many as thirty caterpillars; and the caterpillar death-rate must rise steeply in the neighbourhood of any nest of any of our social wasps. Of these, the common Wasp, *Vespa vulgaris*, and two more of our native species, build under ground, whilst a few others, such as *Vespa sylvestris*, make those nests that look like dirty Chinese lanterns hanging from the branches of trees or bushes. The wasp colony begins in spring when a female who has mated the previous autumn and hidden hibernating through the winter, comes out and makes from wood-pulp "paper" a few cells in which she lays her first eggs. These develop into "workers"—that is, imperfect females—which then help to enlarge the nest and to tend succeeding batches of grubs. The

22

WASPS' NEST
Engraving from James Rennie's *Insect Architecture*, 1838

nest grows in size with the growing population, the busy workers feeding the numerous young on caterpillars all through the summer. When it becomes evident to the workers, or, perhaps, to the mother-female or queen, that the season is so far advanced as to make the rearing of another brood hazardous or impossible, the egg-laying ceases, any grubs that happen to be in the cells are taken out and killed, and the entire winged population enjoys for a few brief weeks, an orgy of well-earned self-indulgence amongst the plums and pears, the jam jars and the marmalade pots, before the first frosts kill them off and the winter rains disintegrate their nest. For the wasp community, unlike the communities of bees and ants, does not survive the season in which it is founded. The fertilised females fly off to crevices in trees, corners of cupboards, folds in curtains, where they hang by their jaws in a dormant state till the following spring.

Autumn is the briefest of the seasons—at least for insects. We hardly and grudgingly recognise its approach in August; for them, it is practically over with September. W. H. Hudson has noted how suddenly the insect tribes disappear. I myself am writing this in the middle of September. Last week wasps were still very numerous and active from two nests in the garden; yesterday only one came for my jam; to-day, after a slight frost, there have been none—though the bees are still busy among the still plentiful flowers, and there will be flies and butterflies for some weeks to come.

"Ivy," says Gilbert White, "is the last flower that supports the hymenopterous and dipterous insects. On sunny days, quite on to November, they swarm on trees covered with this plant; and when they disappear, probably retire under the shelter of its leaves, concealing themselves between its fibres and the trees which it entwines."

23

One remembers Shelley's "yellow bees in the ivy-bloom." And, because, though we may not welcome autumn, we are reluctant to let it go, let us glance back at a group of insects in an autumn field :

> Some climb the stubble, others try the power,
> And compass of their wings, by many a flight,
> From herb to herb and onward draw, as if
> They wished to join the reapers in their talk :
> Some less ambitious, less aspiring, crawl
> In silence, on the thread-bare soil, they seek
> No higher ground. Here harmless butterflies
> Of every wing, wander among the sheaves,
> The forest and the field their home. Here too,
> The humble-bee, proud monarch of the flies,
> At will perambulates. Far from his realms,
> The flowery heath and gloomy glens he's come
> To seek fresh pasturage among the sheaves.
> Ah ! happy insects, happy flies no care
> Is yours. Nought know ye of a lover's pain.

So wrote the Pembrokeshire peasant, Thomas Francis, who became an English schoolmaster and whose *Harvest Day*, published in 1859, is worth reading not because it contains some of the most comically ham-handed blank-verse lines in the language, but because Francis was in his very small way a true poet and a loving observer of nature.

But the sun will not stand still, and winter must come. Of winter John Leonard Knapp says in his pleasant *Journal of a Naturalist*, written early last century under the influence of the *Natural History of Selborne*:

"Winter takes from us all the gay world of the meads, the sylphs that hover over our flowers, that steal our sweets, that creep, or gently wing their way in glittering splendour around us; and of all the miraculous creatures that sported their hour in the sunny beam, the winter gnat (*Tipula hiemalis*) alone remains to frolic in some rare and partial gleam."

He might also have mentioned, as frolicing in the rare and partial gleam of a street-lamp perhaps, the males of the Winter moth, *Cheimatobia brumata* whose almost wingless females are a bane to pomologists. And, of course, there is the unpleasant Cockroach or "black-beetle"—which is not a beetle— and the charming Cricket-by-the-hearth, *Gryllus domesticus*—neither of them truly indigenous British insects. But in the main, winter means death or suspended animation for nearly all our insects. Some survive it as eggs or as chrysalids, some, like the queen wasp, by going into winter quarters and to sleep. Yet such, after all, is our climate that in most winters some insect or other may be met with on good days between Guy Fawkes and Saint Valentine; and then, however common it may be between St. Valentine and Guy Fawkes, it takes on the colour of rarity and is worth entering in your diary.

BIRCH WEEVILS: *CURCULIO BETULAE*
Coloured engraving by E. Donovan from his *Natural History of British Insects*, 1794

MAGPIE OR CURRANT MOTH: *PHALAENA GROSSULARIATA*
Coloured engraving by E. Donovan from his *Natural History of British Insects*, 1813

INSECTS AND THE ENGLISHMAN

WE have seen that wasps hardly deserve all the hard things that are said of them and done to them. But there are many insects of whom little good can be written. The fact puzzled some of the older naturalists, with their reverent but anthropocentric stand-point. To quote the *Journal of a Naturalist* again :

"The designs of Supreme Intelligence in the creation and preservation of the insect world, and the regulations and appointments whereby their increase or decrease is maintained, and periodical appearance prescribed, are among the most perplexing considerations of natural history."

That is representative of the eighteenth century and early nineteenth century attitude. Men could still take an optimistic view, believing that if only they knew enough they would find that God had created all things for the benefit of Man. Perhaps they were right. But in the meantime scientists have grown more cynical. Here is Professor Balfour-Browne : "What use has such an insect as the flea ?" the professor asks, and answers, "Its parasitic habit, by which, in its adult stage, it sucks the blood of animals and birds, although of no use to us, is of the greatest use to the germs of plague, since these germs pass from rat to rat and rat to man though the agency of the rat flea, which sucks the blood infected with the germs from one host and regurgitates some of it with the germs into another."

So, it all depends on how you look at it. To discover the designs of Supreme Intelligence we may, in sympathetic disillusion, have to consider the interests of the plague germ. It sounds unlikely and I doubt if it is true. But, without going into theology, some of these insects are, in all conscience, troublesome enough. Leaving fleas aside for the moment, there is little, so far as I know, to be said for the common, all-too-common, Clothes Moth.

The Clothes Moth is that member of the Lepidopterous tribe with which most people in these urbanised days are probably most familiar. The moths are conveniently, but not strictly scientifically, separated from their cousins the butterflies by various structural and habitual characteristics, one of which is that they tend to appear only after dark. So the Clothes Moth is seldom seen by day, except when one has occasion to shake out a pile of stored blankets, or put on an old coat that has long been hanging in a cupboard. Then the little creature, looking like an ear of chaff, will be seen crawling or fluttering away. The moth itself is not the immediate cause of the holes that have been made. These are the result of the hungry feeding of the grub, which also may frequently be found and, if you can restrain yourself, watched. But first it must be extracted from its tubular tent, when it will set to to make a new one from the cloth. Moth larvæ only feed on fabrics of animal origin—that is to say, roughly speaking, wool or fur—so that there is no point in wasting camphor-balls on linen sheets or cotton shirts or artificial silk stockings. If these things are found eaten into holes, it is probably by wood lice or mice or fungus or something else that is not an insect. Not that there are not plenty of insects that do destroy vegetable substances in houses —particularly wood. Of these, "worm" is, perhaps, the commonest—and will serve as an example.

What furniture dealers and church restorers call "worms" are really the larvæ of a small beetle, about a quarter of an inch long, probably *Anobium domesticum* in the case of furniture, which feed on old wood, riddling its interior with burrows and sending out little showers of wood dust on to the floor. There is another species of anobium which attacks books, and this, from my personal point of view, is a more serious matter—it is no joke to find my first edition of *The Seasons* bored straight through from cover to cover. The beetle that most commonly destroys the structural woodwork of old buildings is the Death Watch, *Xestobium tesselatum*, and the clicking noise, that can be heard where it is present, is Xestobium calling to its mate by bumping its little head against the wood. I know of no redeeming feature connected with these beetles, and they are extremely hard to be rid of. Another rather unattractive insect is my old friend the Warble fly (*Hypoderma bovis* or *Hypoderma lineatum*). These are the flies that make cattle "gad" during the summer. Thomson refers to the moment when :

"Perchance a flight of angry gad-flies fasten on the herd"

and Gilbert White spoke of Thomson as "a nice observer of natural circumstances;" but here he failed to observe nicely, for the Warble or gad-fly attacks singly and, what is curious since cattle will "gad" before they are touched, noiselessly—at least to the human ear. It was only during the time when I was working on them that the life-history of the Warble flies was fully followed out, and it is still frequently given wrongly in books. The female attaches her eggs very neatly to the hairs on the legs of the cattle.

GAD FLY OR SHEEP BOT-FLY: *Oestrus Ovis*
Coloured engraving by E. Donovan from his *Natural History of British Insects*, 1813

When the young larva hatches it bores its way through the skin and enters the animal's bloodstream. It next appears, after about nine weeks, as quite a large maggot in the tissues of the æsophagus. From the throat, it works its way through the body, growing as it goes, until it comes up as a full-sized larva or "warble" as big as the top of one's thumb under the skin of the back. It then breaks through the skin and pupates in the ground. Not a pleasant progress, but one that, oddly enough, does not seem to trouble the cattle, once it has got under way, though it does great commercial damage to their hides.

From insects that affect the Englishman's goods and chattels, let us turn for a moment to a few of those with which—(so close are they one should almost say with *whom*)—he is most intimate.

Oliver Goldsmith was neither an observant nor a well-informed naturalist. "The savages of Canada knew no enemies but the prowling bear or the insidious tiger." That Canadian tiger was not the least of his solecisms. But of certain insects he had first-hand knowledge, enemies nearer than Canada and quite as insidious as the tiger. For he lived in Ireland and in England, and he travelled on the Continent in an age which knew nothing of vacuum cleaners nor even of Keating's Powder. So that his remarks on the comparative numbers and virulence of English and foreign fleas may be taken as authentic—his Irish origin saving him from any suspicion of patriotic prejudice. In his *History of the Earth and Animated Nature* he has a chapter on the flea in which he says:

BED-BUG : *Cimex Lectularius*
Coloured engraving by John Curtis from
his *British Entomology*, 1835

"There are few but are well informed of the agility and blood-thirsty disposition of the flea. This insect is found in every part of the world, but bites with greater severity in some countries than in others. Its numbers in Italy and France are much greater than in England; and yet its bite is 'much more troublesome here than I have found it in any other place."

My own experience neither confirms nor conflicts with Goldsmith's, for mercifully, fleas do not bite me. I can, however, sympathise with the old lady who remarked, "It isn't their biting I mind at all, but their continual tramping round and round" —their tramping has not seldom come between me and my sleep.

Fleas are, morphologically, in many ways similar to flies from whom they are supposed to have descended in the course of an age-long evolutionary process, and in a matter of comparative

28

detail such as this it may well be so. But my personal heresy is that I can no longer believe in the "evolutionary process"—at least, not on the scale that is required by modern biological theory. I hope that I am not backward in honouring Charles Darwin. His *Origin of Species* is not only a classic of natural science, but also a classic of nineteenth century English literature. Yet, when one turns from its fascinating and persuasive thesis to meditate upon the structure of the Bee and, beyond the Bee, upon the Hive, and further upon all the intricate relationships of the insect world, then the hypothesis of Darwin in the *Origin of Species* seems a less likely guess than, say, the hypothesis attributed to Moses in the first chapter of *Genesis*. But my philosophic opinions are, perhaps, of less interest than my observations—or than Goldsmith's. After his chapter on fleas he has one on "the Bug Kind." And here again he is able, speaking from experience, to say that "happily for Great Britain, bugs multiply less in these islands than in any part of the

YELLOW BAT'S FLEA: *Ceratophyllus Elongatus*
Coloured engraving by John Curtis from his *British Entomology*, 1832

Continent." It is true that there were probably fewer bugs in England at that time than elsewhere, because the "Mahogany Flat," as it is unaffectionately called in London, is not one of our indigenous insects but an immigrant who seems to have become naturalised during the sixteenth century.

My only direct experience of bed-bugs is somewhat oblique. I was once staying, as the guest of a well-known painter, in a rather expensive hotel. In the morning, after our first night, my friend called me into his bedroom and showed me, on a card under his tooth-glass, half-a-dozen or more creatures which could only be specimens of *Cimex lectularius*. Having failed to make much impression either with their Latin name or with a demonstration of their pictorial qualities through a pocket lens, I took them to the Management. The Management affected outraged incredulity, but next night I found that I, who had slept peacefully enough, had been moved into the best bedroom in the house—my friend remaining where he had been. Next day we sought lodging elsewhere, for, as Goldsmith had discovered two centuries earlier, neither attack nor elastic defence will avail against the bed-bug.

It is almost embarrassing to think of animals so repellent as bed-bugs finding one another attractive, yet Goldsmith particularly noted their amorous propensities. There is, however, a more elegant member of the Bug kind whose sex-appeal one may contemplate without disgust. It is a cousin of our Mahogany Flat—though not so close a cousin as the Rev. Gilbert White, who thus describes it, believed :

"August 12, 1775.—Cimices lineares are now in high copulation on ponds and pools. The females, who vastly exceed the males in bulk, dart and shoot along on the surface of the water with the males on their backs. When the female chooses to be disengaged, she rears, and jumps, and plunges like an unruly colt; the lover, thus dismounted, soon finds a new mate. The females, as fast as their curiosities are satisfied, retire to another part of the lake. Hence the sexes are found separate, except when generation is going on." Entomologists no longer place these pond skaters in the genus *Cimex*. The species that White so nicely describes is now known as *Gerris lacustris*.

I do not know that *Gerris* is of any utilitarian value to man, but it does no harm and is at least aesthetically not unpleasing. It may serve, therefore, as a neutral passage from the pure pests to consideration of a few of the many useful insects.

In their degree, all insects that burrow in the soil may be counted as valuable irrigators, though some, such as the larvæ of the Daddy-longlegs, do more harm than good. Among those that certainly do more good than harm, since they are scavengers as well as diggers and manurers of the soil, are the well-known and beautiful Burying Beetles. The French naturalist, J. H. Fabre, has written of these in his book, *The Glow-worm and Other Beetles*. I hope I need no excuse for referring to this great Frenchman in a book on English Insects. As observer, experimenter, and interpreter, he deserves to rank with Darwin. He lived, 1823 to 1915, even longer than Kirby.

Most country people have seen the Burying Beetles—large red-and-black insects—round the dead body of a mouse or a bird in which they propose to lay their eggs. But first they must get the corpse under ground, and this they do by digging away the earth below it and, by supporting its weight on their own backs, sinking it to a depth of several inches. If the ground on which they find the dead body is too hard, and if there is soft ground in the immediate neighbourhood, the beetles will move the body to a more suitable position. If the beetles, feeling the weight taken off their backs, find that the body has become supported on small roots, they will cut through these with their jaws. Fabre tied up a dead body with string, so that it could not descend of its own weight, and this, too, the beetles cut. He then tied it up with wire, attached to the dead animal's foot, when the beetles, unable to gnaw through the wire, gnawed through the foot instead. Fabre denied that such activities of the Burying Beetles were signs of intelligence or of any capacity to think out ways of dealing with an unexpected situation, and he was probably right. But another French entomologist of first-class standing, Professor E. L.

GRAVEDIGGER BEETLE: *Necrophorus Germanicus*
Coloured engraving by John Curtis from his *British Entomology*, 1825

Bouvier, in his book on *The Psychic Life of Insects*, published in 1922, came to the conclusion that "all the higher instincts had originally an intellectual quality," and that they were "acquired by an intelligent apprenticeship." I suppose it all depends on how you define that rather elusive term "intelligence." I have never watched the Burying Beetles as Fabre did, but anyone who has considered the minutiæ rather than the large-scale aspects of insect behaviour as they are displayed by Ants, say, in a Berkshire pine-wood on a summer afternoon, will hardly deny to some insects degrees and differences of technical ability, more and less successful acts of choice, and other signs of what we can only call "intelligence" as we apply the word to ourselves—and this, without prejudice to the psychic activities of the ants-nest or the bee-hive as a whole, which is a separate problem raised by a growing tendency to look on the colony itself rather than the individual ant or bee as the psychological unit among the social *Hymenoptera*.

Of all the obviously useful insects in this country, Bees are the most spectacular example. With the exception of the Silk-worm moth, they are man's only domestic insects—or anyhow, remembering the fleas and bugs, the only insects he has willingly domesticated. And he has done so, of course, for the sake of their honey and their wax—sweetness and light, in fact.

There still seems to be some doubt as to whether the Honey-bee, *Apis mellifica*, is indigenous in its wild state in this country; but it has been domesticated in Europe for over two thousand years, and for over a thousand in

31

these islands. The Venerable Bede mentions Ireland as being "rich in milk and honey"—*Hibernia dives lactis ac mellis insula*—and if that was true of Ireland in the seventh century it must have been no less true of England at an even earlier date. Certainly from the most ancient times Bees have been the subject of profound interest. Pliny says that Aristomachus of Soles spent fifty-eight years in studying them—though how he did it or to what effect is not very clear, since it is only with the invention of glass observation-hives by an Italian in 1712 that the proper study of bees can be said to have begun. During the eighteenth century, as casual references by Laurence Sterne and other writers show, these glass hives became fairly common objects in England, and English entomologists were among the first scientific bee-watchers. The Rev. John Thorley published his *Melissologia, or Female Monarchy; being an Enquiry into the Nature, Order, and Government of the Bees* in 1744: and Thomas Wildman, his *Treatise on the Management of Bees; with the Natural History of Wasps and Hornets*, in 1768. Neither of these apiarists is mentioned in the D.N.B., nor is William Gould, whose *English Ants* appeared in 1747; and one may note in passing that that invaluable work of reference is decidedly stingy in its estimate of entomological eminence. Thorley was an acute observer, and, perhaps, the first to discover the true nature and mode of production of the wax from which the honey-comb is made; and Wildman's book is "a very curious publication, and well deserves the attention of every friend to ingenious industry," as a contemporary review said of it. But since the middle of the eighteenth century the literature on Bees and Bee-keeping has become simply monumental. The subject has been written up in all its aspects, from the merely fanciful, through the severely scientific, to the strictly commercial, in a flood of books which shows no sign of stopping. And accurate observation has gone hand in hand with both intelligent and romantic speculation. Bees have been credited with almost superhuman intellectual faculties; and they have been degraded to the condition of even more automatic automata than the "behaviourist" psychologists would have us men to be. They were long supposed to be mathematicians of genius :

> The bee observe;
> She too an artist is, and laughs at man,
> Who calls on rules the sightly hexagon
> With truth to form; a cunning architect,
> Who at the roof begins her golden work,
> And builds without foundation. How she toils.

So wrote the Rev. James Hurdis, D.D., and Professor of Poetry in the University of Oxford—a better poet than that quotation shows, and always a keen observer of natural phenomena. The mystery of the bee's cell remains. Some nineteenth century materialist thought he had solved it when he observed that a packet of cylindrical candles when warmed and pressed together formed

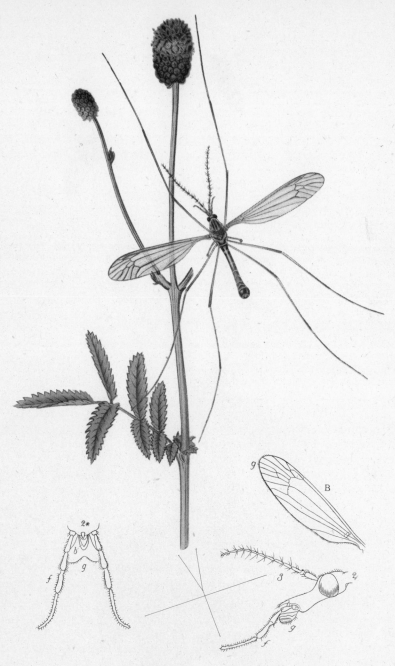

CRANE-FLY: *TIPULA LONGICORNIS*
Coloured engraving by John Curtis from his *British Entomology*, 1834

ANCHOR-FACED WASP: *VESPA RUFA*

Coloured engraving by John Curtis from his *British Entomology*, 1839

a packet of hexagonal candles, but he had not observed the bees at their job. It is unnecessary to describe once again the astonishing economy of the hive. It is an awe-inspiring, not to say a frightening, subject. Who would live in such a community? Who could ever make friends with an *Apis mellifica*? As Sir Arthur Shipley, a great modern authority, has said, "One has a feeling that one might appeal to the better instincts of a bumble-bee, but that it would be perfectly useless to make such an appeal to a honey-bee" —even if one dared suppose there to be better instincts. For the honey-bee is in almost every respect a paragon of Christian virtue crossed with Marxian virtue—a communist altruist of the purest water—and yet—it is, perhaps, just our instinctive recoil from what the Italian observation-hive has shown us that reconciles us to our own inefficient liberal democracy.

To Englishmen of but a few generations back honey was the only available sweetening material. It is, of course, from the bee's point of view, a manufactured substance—not less so than marmalade. Honey, as such, does not occur in "nature"—not even in the honey-suckle. Flowers produce nectar, which is of quite a different texture and composition from the bee-made honey. In the course of time, honey has accumulated a great deal of lore— both folk and culinary. It was the chief ingredient of the intoxicating drink known as mead and of the clarre of Chaucer's day. Our "Honey-moon" derives from an ancient Saxon custom of drinking quantities of hydromel, or honey-wine, for thirty days after marriage; and honey is still supposed to have mild aphrodisiac properties. Attila the Hun died from drinking too much hydromel. Honey also had magical life-giving properties, derived, perhaps in part from its golden colour (gold was a life-giving substance with the ancients), and partly from the fact that it does not, from the minute quantities of formic acid which it contains, deteriorate with age. Besides which, it was (and is) beneficial for the dressing of wounds. In some fertility-rites the Moon was a bee, and according to Porphyry the Nymphs appeared as bees—hence, it may be, the bee pupæ are still called nymphs.

Here is a seventeenth century recipe for Mead :

"To every ten quarts of water take a quart of honey and one pound of loaf sugar. Let the water be boiling before you put the honey in. Let it boil till no scum arises, which will be a quarter of an hour. Then put it into your mug you intend to keep it in which must have a tap in it. Then squeeze four or five lemons and half the peels, twenty cloves, two races of ginger, two or three sprigs of Rosemary, and a little balm. Put juice and spices and herbs into the pot first, and then pour the liquor hot upon it, and stop it with a cloth to keep the steam in. When it is milk-warm put in two spoonsful of barm spread upon toasted bread put in warm. Let it stand three or four days, stirring once a day. Then close it up and let it stand a fortnight and bottle it."

Though we no longer make much use of such recipes, Bees are still among the most valuable of our insects—especially during war-time sugar-shortages.

INSECTS AND ENGLISH LITERATURE

OFFHAND, I do not remember that Chaucer, who loved flowers and gardens, has any reference to insects, and the middle-ages in general do not seem to have taken much overt account of them. This may be due to the cultural influence of the Hebrews (among whom Beelzebub was Prince of Flies) on Christian literature. I think Origen was the only one of the Church Fathers who was anything of an entomologist, and Origen has always been tinged with ecclesiastical suspicion.

Insects begin to be glanced at, still a little askance it is true, in the poetry of the 16th century. Spenser has his "swarme of gnats at eventide" (those were Irish gnats, though), and there are plenty of insects in Shakespeare. But Shakespeare did not really care for them, and his carelessness is evident in nearly all his references, as when he supposes the glow-worm to glow with his eyes. Sir Thomas Browne, also, ill-observed the birth of a butterfly: "In the aurelian metamorphosis," he says, "the head of the canker becomes the tail of the butterfly." Thereafter, insects may be found making their contribution to our literature—never as freely as flowers, but substantially if often obliquely. The young Donne, observing a flea, seized on it not to drown it, but to turn it to account in his amorous designs:

> Marke but this flea, and marke in this,
> How little that which thou deny'st me is;
> It suck'd me first, and now sucks thee,
> And in this flea, our two bloods mingled bee;
> Thou know'st that this cannot be said
> A sinne, nor shame, nor losse of maidenhead . .

Carew made the same sort of graceful play with a Fly in his Mistress's Eye and with a Bee in Celia's Bosom.

34

The 18th century took to insects, both as objects of beauty and interest in their own right, and also speculatively and to the glory of God. Biological philosophy at that time was dominated by a conception of "The Chain of Being" in which insects had their essential and not insignificant place. It is set forth in a noble poem addressed by Benjamin Stillingfleet to Thomas Pennant. After mentioning some of the more utilitarian aspects of Creation, "Not these alone," he says:

> Which strike ev'n eyes incurious, but each moss,
> Each shell, each crawling insect holds a rank
> Important in the plan of Him, who fram'd
> This scale of beings; holds a rank, which lost
> Would break the chain, and leave behind a gap
> Which Nature's self would rue.

The same thesis occurs in Thomson and Pope. Paley in his *Natural Theology* gives considerable space to insects. They had, in fact, become respectable. Gray loved them to the extent of turning Linnæus's entomology into Latin verse. Everyone remembers, "where the beetle wheels his droning flight," and he mentions the appearance of the White Butterfly, of Gnats, and of the Ladybird, in his letters. But what deeply touched his enthusiasm was a present of foreign insects :

"Here is Mr. Foljambe, has got a flying hobgoblin from the East Indies, and a power of rarities, and then he has given me such a phalæna, with looking glasses in its wings, and a queen of the white ants, whose belly alone is as big as many hundred of her subjects, I do not mean their bellies only, but their whole persons; and yet her tetons and her legs are no bigger than other people's. Oh, she is a jewel of a pismire !"

And elsewhere, less breathlessly and more scientifically, he describes his jewel in fuller detail.

Indeed the Augustan period was certainly insect-conscious, from Addison with his rather second-hand Ants to William Smyth, Professor of Modern History at Cambridge, who, in his *English Lyrics* of 1797, has a charming poem to a Bee, and Erasmus Darwin, who, two years later, wrote this beautiful invocation :

> Stay thy soft murmuring waters, gentle Rill;
> Hush, whispering Winds; ye rustling Leaves, be still;
> Rest, silver Butterflies, your quivering wings;
> Alight, ye Beetles, from your airy rings;
> Ye painted Moths, your gold-eyed plumage furl,
> Bow your wide horns, your spiral trunks uncurl;
> Glitter, ye Glow-worms, on your mossy beds;
> Descend, ye Spiders, on your lengthened threads;
> Slide here, ye horned Snails, with varnished shells;
> Ye Bee-nymphs, listen in your waxen cells !

35

During the nineteenth century insects become almost commonplace both in prose and verse. John Clare and Charles Tennyson-Turner are, I suppose, the most entomological of our poets. Wordsworth admonishes a robin for chasing a butterfly, and himself captures a glow-worm for Dorothy in his one entirely delightful and non-moralising insect poem :

> Among all lovely things my Love had been;
> Had noted well the stars, all flowers that grew
> About her home; but she had never seen
> A glow-worm, never one, and this I knew.

So, finding one, he took it home on horseback and put it in his orchard.

> The whole next day I hoped, and hoped with fear;
> At night the glow-worm shone beneath the tree;
> I led my Lucy to the spot, "Look here,"
> Oh ! joy it was for her, and joy for me.

That Dorothy herself had never seen a glow-worm is significant. Accurate observer though she was, I do not think she mentions insects, or hardly ever, in her *Journal*. And for Wordsworth himself, that greatest of poets, they were rather apt to remind him of "My father's family" or some other boring irrelevance.

And the Victorian prose-writers entomologised as assiduously as the poets. The natural-history observation in such a book as Kingsley's *Water Babies* is minutely, not to say microscopically, accurate. Curiously enough, he falls down over one of his most dramatic set pieces—the metamorphosis of the Dragon-fly : •

"Tom stood still and watched him. And he swelled himself, and puffed, and stretched himself out stiff and at last—crack, puff, bang—he opened all down his back, and then up to the top of his head.

"And out of his inside came the most slender: elegant, soft creature, as soft and smooth as Tom, but very pale and weak, like a little child who has been ill a long time in a dark room. It moved its legs very feebly, and looked about it half ashamed; and then it began walking slowly up a grass stem to the top of the water.

"Tom was so astonished that he never said a word; but he stared with all his eyes. And he went up to the top of the water too, and peeped out to see what would happen.

"And as the creature sat in the warm, bright sun a wonderful change came over it. It grew strong and firm; the most lovely colours began to show on its body, blue and yellow and black, spots and bars and rings; out of its back rose four great wings of bright brown gauze; and its eyes grew so large that they filled all its head, and shone like ten thousand diamonds."

A very fine specimen, probably of *Æschna cyanea*, in fact. But, though I myself have never had the luck, even after much patient watching by Hert-

36

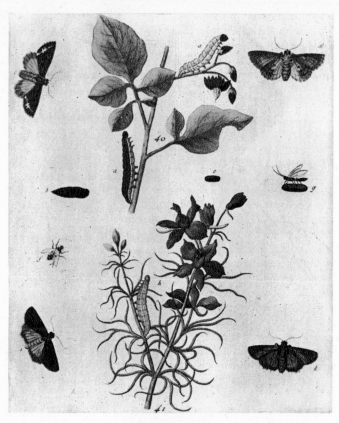

MOTHS AND FLIES
Coloured engraving by Eleazar Albin from his *Natural History of English Insects*, 1720

fordshire ponds in my schooldays, to see the emergence of the perfect
insect from the dragon-fly grub (the dragon-fly is among the relatively few
insects that do not pass through a pupal stage), I have many times found
the empty larval skins clinging to grasses well above the water-line, and all
the books confirm the obvious deduction that the transformation from grub
to dragon-fly never takes place whilst the grub is in the water. How Kingsley,
who ranks as a good field naturalist, as well as a man of letters, came to make
such a mistake I cannot imagine. On the manners and habits of Cadis-worms
(the case-building aquatic larvæ of the *Trichoptera*) and on many other
animals, some of them almost invisible to the naked eye, *The Water Babies*
may be taken, so far as it goes, as an accurate guide. Another small mistake
that has troubled some readers is that both Cowper and Clare, I think
Thomson also, speak of the Glow-worm as "he," when as everyone is sup-

37

posed to know, the true "glow-worm" is the wingless female of the beetle, *Lampyris noctiluca*. Actually, the winged male is sometimes faintly luminous (so, too, are the eggs and larvæ), but there is no doubt that Cowper, probably from ignorance, and Clare, more likely from a rural indifference to pronouns which permits even a hen to be "he" on occasion, were both in error. It is not a matter of much importance, but it's a safe bet that if Crabbe mentions Glow-worms, as he well may, he does so correctly.

Insects become more and more plentiful, both in prose and verse, towards the end of the Victorian time and up to the interval between the Great Wars. Galsworthy, Kipling and Hardy, among novelists; W. H. Hudson and Richard Jefferies, among prose-writers who were not professional scientists; W. H. Davies and Edmund Blunden, conspicuously, among the "Georgian" poets, with Andrew Young and J. C. Snaith a little later, were all careful observers and delightful recorders. In the restless twenty years between 1919 and 1939, poets and writers in general were not much disposed to use their eyes—at least, to most of them insects seemed insignificant by comparison with slums and with political and philosophical problems. Latterly there are signs—welcome signs, I must confess—of a change. People are once more turning their attention and their steps toward the English countryside, and not merely as more or less curious week-enders. Poets are again beginning to look at things, even with a pocket-lens. Sidney Keyes, one of the best poets and most lamented casualties of the Second World War could "note the green-fly working on the rose," and a moment's search through the latest contemporary writing would produce plenty of additional evidence. And, thanks not only to their own awakened powers of observation, but to the general enlightenment brought about by the very many excellent hand-books on popular entomology, the amateurs are no longer likely to irritate the professionals, as Samuel Rogers irritated William Kirby by making his Bee:

> With conscious truth retrace the mazy clue
> Of varied scents that charm'd her as she flew.

The Editor of *The Tailor and Cutter* at the Royal Academy could not be more pained than the Rev. Mr. Kirby was at that.

So much for a rough sketch of Insects in English Literature. I would not make an extravagant claim for these insect poems and prose passages. A butterfly is not a Sunset, nor an ant-hill an Alp, nor a swarm of bees an Atlantic storm; nor has any insect the rich emblematic associations of the Rose and the Lily, the Nightingale and the Skylark. The Sublime is the thing, no doubt. But the merely pretty may have its peculiar, enduring and endearing perfections. And so it can happen that, without, I hope, blinding myself to a right scale of values, I may find myself on six days out of the seven reading the poetry of John Clare or Charles Tennyson-Turner or Ebenezer Elliott rather than *Paradise Lost* or *The Ring and the Book* (not that Milton and Browning have not their insects too)—just as one might, or, still

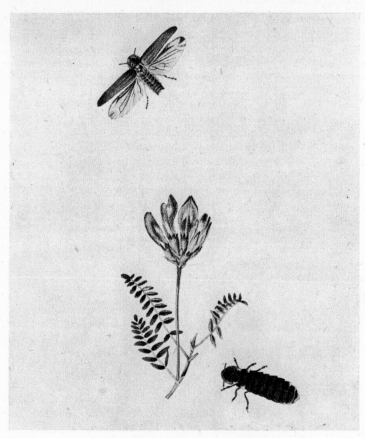

GLOW-WORM: *Lampyris Noctiluca*
Coloured engraving by John Curtis from his *British Entomology*, 1838

speaking for myself, I might, prefer to hang on my intimate walls an original coloured engraving by John Curtis or one of the Sowerbys rather than anything by your Braques and Picassos—superb artists though I recognise these last to be. English literature is almost embarrassingly rich, along its main roads, but also down its byways; and often it may be more restful and even more exciting to follow some lane that leads only into a field or a wood—especially if one's interests are not solely and severely in artistic superlatives.

English Insects, then? At the beginning I suggested that there is nothing to distinguish the English from the un-English specimen; but here, though I have quoted much already, here to end up with is a little group of indubitably English insects—English insects preserved in English amber—enshrined by English writers in English words.

39

The first is by the Rev. William Lisle Bowles, Canon of St. Paul's and Rector of Bremhill in Wiltshire, and it is one of the "compositions that were," he says, "written originally to be learned by heart by poor children of my own parish, who have been instructed every Sunday through the summer, on the garden lawn before the parsonage house, by Mrs. Bowles." The summer in question was one in the early eighteen-twenties.

THE GLOW-WORM

Oh, what is this which shines so bright,
    And in the lonely place
Hangs out his small green lamp at night,
    The dewy bank to grace !
It is a glow-worm, still and pale,
    It shines the whole night long,
When only stars, O nightingale,
    Seem listening to thy song !
And so amid the world's cold night,
    Through good report or ill,
Shines out the humble Christian's light,
    As lonely and as still.

Coleridge and Wordsworth had noticed before that the Glow-worm's light is green.

Then there is the strange game at dice on Egdon Heath in Thomas Hardy's *Return of the Native*. It was pitch dark. The protagonists in the game were Wildeve and Christian with Venn intervening. A Death's-head moth had extinguished the light from their lantern:

"As their eyes grew accustomed to the darkness they perceived faint greenish points of light among the grass and fern. These lights dotted the hillside like stars of low magnitude.

" 'Ah—glow-worms,' said Wildeve. 'Wait a minute. We can continue the game.'

"Venn sat still, and his companion went hither and thither till he had gathered thirteen glow-worms—as many as he could find in a space of four or five minutes—upon a foxglove leaf which he pulled for the purpose. The reddleman vented a low humorous laugh when he saw his adversary return with these. 'Determined to go on, then ?' he said drily.

" 'I always am !' said Wildeve angrily. And shaking the glow-worms from the leaf he ranged them with a trembling hand in a circle on the stone, leaving a space in the middle for the descent of the dice-box, over which the thirteen tiny lamps threw a pale phosphoric shine. The game was again renewed. It happened to be that season of the year at which glow-worms put forth their greatest brilliancy, and the light they yielded was more than ample for the purpose, since it is possible on such nights to read the hand-writing of a letter by the light of two or three."

PEACOCK, SMALL TORTOISESHELL AND COMMA BUTTERFLIES
VANESSA IO, VANESSA URTICAE AND *VANESSA C.—ALBUM*
Ink and wash drawing by Vere Temple
By courtesy of the Artist

DRAGONFLIES

Agrion splendens, f.   *Agrion splendens, m.*

Libellula Fulva, m.

Nymph Case of *agrion splendens*   Parasitic Wasp: *Pimpla instigator*

Pencil and wash drawing by Vere Temple

By courtesy of the Artist

In corroboration of that last statement here is a passage from the *Journal of Summer Time in the Country* published by the Rev. R. A. Willmott in 1849:

"But I have been turning glow-worms to a use this evening, which no naturalist probably ever thought of—reading the Psalms by their cool green radiance. I placed six of the most luminous insects I could find in the grass, at the top of the page; moving them from verse to verse, as I descended. The experiment was perfectly successful. Each letter became clear and legible, making me feel deeply and gratefully the inner life of the Psalmist's adoration."

Lampyris noctiluca bulks relatively large in literature. We will leave her with a famous poem that does not quite take the shine out of Bowles's— Marvell's.

THE MOWER TO THE GLO-WORMS

Ye living lamps, by whose dear light
    The Nightingale does sit so late,
And studying all the Summer-night,
    Her matchless songs does meditate;

Ye Country Comets, that portend
    No War, nor Princes funeral,
Shining unto no higher end,
    Than to presage a Grasses fall;

Ye Glo-worms, whose officious Flame
    To wandering Mowers shows the way,
That in the Night have lost their aim,
    And after foolish Fires do stray;

Your courteous Lights in vain you wast,
    Since *Juliana* here is come,
For She my Mind hath so displac'd
    That I shall never find my home.

One does not suspect Burke of being much of a naturalist, until one remembers his admiration for Crabbe, but at some time the music of Grasshoppers must have disturbed his *Reflections on the French Revolution*, for in that unlikely book he wrote:

"Because half a dozen grasshoppers under a fern make the field ring with their importunate chink, whilst thousands of great cattle, reposed beneath the shadow of the British oak, chew the cud and are silent, pray do not imagine that those who make the noise are the only inhabitants of the field; that, of course, they are many in number; or that, after all, they are other than the little, shrivelled, meagre, hopping, though loud and troublesome *insects* of the hour."

A thousand cattle sound like over-stocking for an English field, but no doubt Burke made his point. Lovelace was more disinterested in his poem:

O Thou that swing'st upon the waving ear
    Of some well-filled oaten beard,
Drunk every night with a delicious tear
    Dropt thee from Heaven, where now th'art rear'd !

The joys of earth and air are thine entire,
    That with thy feet and wings dost hop and fly;
And when thy poppy works, thou dost retire
    To thy carved acorn-bed to lie.

Up with the day, the Sun thou welcom'st then,
    Sport'st in the gilt plaits of his beams,
And all these merry days mak'st merry men
    Thyself, and melancholy streams.

Keats's sonnet beginning "The poetry of earth is never dead" is well known, and I prefer to quote Leigh Hunt's poem written at the same time :

TO THE GRASSHOPPER AND THE CRICKET

Green little vaulter in the sunny grass,
    Catching your heart up in the feel of June,
    Sole voice that's heard amidst the lazy noon,
When even the bees lag at the summoning brass.
And you, warm little housekeeper, who class
    With those who think the candles come too soon,
    Loving the fire, and with your tricksome tune
Nick the glad silent moments as they pass;
Oh sweet and tiny cousins, that belong,
    One to the fields, the other to the hearth,
Both have your sunshine; both, though small, are strong
    At your clear hearts; and both seem given to earth
To ring in thoughtful ears this natural song—
    In doors and out, summer and winter, Mirth.

It would be pleasant to copy out the bit about Bees in chapter XXI of Borrow's *Romany Rye*, but there are swarms, hives, bonnets-full of bees in prose and verse. Earwigs are not so common, but my friend, D. J. O'Sullivan, poet, naturalist, and lighthouse-keeper, has written much about them. This is an extract from *Earwig* published in 1942 :

"Vestal February. The nymph-earwig slowly emerged from its egg, a tricky business at the best of times. First its mouth-pieces appeared, then its head, fore-legs and shoulders. It wriggled. Two more legs appeared. It lay quiet for a moment. Then the delicate antennæ lying folded flat across its

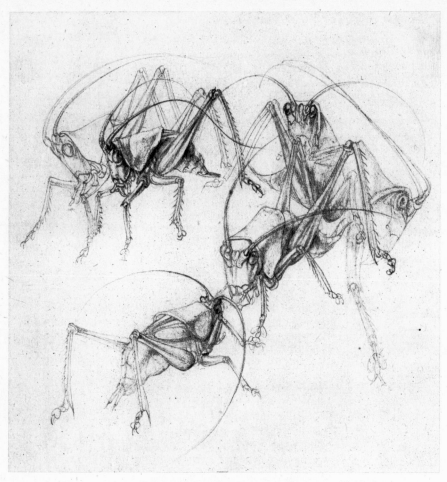

NYMPH OF THE GREAT GREEN GRASSHOPPER: *Tettigonia Viridissima*
Pencil drawing by Vere Temple

veinless elytra became erect. It drew out its hind legs and stood up. The eggshell still concealed its tail forceps. It wriggled again. The forceps became visible. They were two tiny hair-like appendages touching all the way from base to tip and denoting a female, ghost-like and frail. Slowly her body began to change colour. A tiny pin-point of lead-blue appeared at the extremity of her tail, and, enlarging, spread like a blob of spilt ink through the seven visible segments of her body towards her head. After one hour she was no longer ghost-like. After two hours she was as black and lustrous as a sloe. She ate her egg and went to sleep."

The further adventures of that earwig were as exciting as anything in Fabre or Thomson-Seton. She was an Ulster earwig, but Ulster is near enough to England.

Tennyson in *The Two Voices* has a correctly witnessed Dragon-fly birth :

> To-day I saw the dragon-fly
> Come from the wells where he did lie.
>
> An inner impulse rent the veil
> Of his old husk; from head to tail
> Came out clear plates of sapphire mail.
>
> He dried his wings; like gauze they grew;
> Thro' crofts and pastures wet with dew
> A living rush of light he flew.

Landor also wrote a dragonfly poem ; but John Clare has more insect poems than all the other poets put together. A random choice falls on his song :

CLOCK-A-CLAY

> In the cowslip pips I lie,
> Hidden from the buzzing fly,
> While green grass beneath me lies,
> Pearled with dew like fishes' eyes,
> Here I lie, a clock-a-clay,
> Waiting for the time of day.
>
> While grassy forest quakes surprise,
> And the wild wind sobs and sighs,
> My gold home rocks as like to fall,
> On its pillar green and tall;
> When the pattering rain drives by
> Clock-a-clay keeps warm and dry.
>
> Day by day and night by night,
> All the week I hide from sight;
> In the cowslip pips I lie,
> In rain and dew still warm and dry;
> Day and night, and night and day,
> Red, black-spotted clock-a-clay.
>
> My home shakes in wind and showers,
> Pale green pillar topped with flowers,
> Bending at the wild wind's breath,
> Till I touch the grass beneath;
> Here I live, lone clock-a-clay,
> Watching for the time of day.

THE TRANSFORMATION OF THE LADYBIRD
Engraving from Acheta Domestica's *Episodes of Insect Life*, 1849

Clock-a-clay is Northamptonshire for Ladybird. The poem was written during Clare's last years in a lunatic asylum. Butterflies are nearly as frequent in poetry and prose as Bees are, so are Moths. But the tribe may be represented by Isaac Walton's portrait of a Puss-moth caterpillar :

· "Nay, the very colours of caterpillars are, as one has observed, very elegant and beautiful. I shall, for a taste of the rest, describe one of them; which I will, some time next month, shew you feeding on a willow-tree; and you shall find him punctually to answer this very description : his lips and mouth somewhat yellow; his eyes black as jet; his forehead purple; his feet and hinder parts green; his tail two-forked and black; the whole body stained with a kind of red spots, which run along the neck and shoulder-blade, not unlike the form of a St. Andrew's cross, or the letter X, made thus crosswise, and a white line drawn down his back to his tail; all which add much beauty to his whole body. And it is to me observable, that at a fixed age this caterpillar gives over to eat, and towards winter comes to be covered with a strange shell or crust, called an aurelia; and so lives a kind of dead life, without eating all the winter. And as others of several kinds turn to be several kinds of flies and vermin, the Spring following; so this caterpillar then turns to be a painted butterfly."

I myself have only found Puss-moths on poplars, but no doubt Walton is right and they also inhabit willows. William Oldys, the antiquary, wrote a life of Charles Cotton, part author with Walton of the *Compleat Angler*. He also wrote :

Busy, curious, thirsty Fly.
Gently drink, and drink as I;
Freely welcome to my cup,
Could'st thou sip, and sip it up;
Make the most of Life you may,
Life is short and wears away.
Just alike, both mine and thine,
Hasten quick to their decline;
Thine's a Summer, mine's no more,
Though repeated to threescore;
Threescore Summers when they're gone,
Will appear as short as one.

It is, perhaps, not strange how many of these entomologists, naturalists, and nature-poets were Clergymen. Their entomology and botany went hand in hand with their pastoral duties. They believed that :

He prayeth best who loveth best
All things both great and small,

though that sentiment outraged the rather stern creed of that great naturalist Philip Henry Gosse, F.R.S. As a last insect-poem then, I would have this, appropriate in several ways, by the Rev. Charles Tennyson-Turner :

ON FINDING
A SMALL FLY CRUSHED IN A BOOK

Some hand that never meant to do thee hurt,
Has crushed thee here between these pages pent;
But thou hast left thine own fair monument,
Thy wings gleam out and tell me what thou wert;
Oh ! that the memories, which survive us here,
Were half as lovely as these wings of thine !
Pure relics of a blameless life, that shine
Now thou art gone. Our doom is ever near :
The peril is beside us day by day;
The book will close upon us, it may be,
Just as we lift ourselves to soar away
Upon the summer airs. But, unlike thee,
The closing book may stop our vital breath,
Yet leave no lustre on our page of death.

Professor Lafcadio Hearn, that odd Japanese-Irish-Greek, complained that the English did not write about insects. He was wrong. There they are— Coleoptera, Orthoptera, Odonata, Diptera, Lepidoptera—and with more space, English insects of other natural orders that might have been added to these, for many Englishmen have written curiously and lovingly of their native Hexapoda.

EPILOGUE
FLOWERED AND FIGURED LANDSCAPE

Here all far view's shut out by nettles, docks,
And tall cow-parsley casting pools of shade,
With rivulets of sunlight down their leaves.
The nettle poison-ducts are velvet pile
Of needle-points where the unheedful spider
Runs to seek out a base-line for her web
And, having found a place, unwinds her coil
Of glittering gluey thread, spreading her snair
For any air-born creature, fly, gnat, aphid,
Or parachute of thistledown that falls
Unwanted decoration to her toil;
Her toil now done she waits there in the centre.
Two ants run up a parsley stalk in quest
Of heaven knows what esoteric nectar.
There on that low-hung umbel copulate—
Again with heaven knows what beetle joy—
Two red telephorids, back-side to back,
Seeming more patient than ecstatic in
Their long love-making on their flowery bed.
A ladybird takes flight from her hot stone,
Fearing her home's on fire maybe, but more,
By insect instinct, likely off to find
A blight of greenfly for her future young.
Now, on a moment all those golden-pale
Cascades from pool to pool of shade are gone
As though a tap had been turned off.
                           I know
Unseen a cloud has over-run the sun.

BOOKS

These are among the best books for the amateur entomologist :—
British Insect Life by Edward Step — *The Observer's Book of
British Butterflies* by W. J. Stokes — *A Butterfly Book for the
Pocket* by Edmund Sandars — *The Butterflies of the British Isles*
by Richard South — *The Moths of the British Isles* by Richard
South (2 vols.) — *British Beetles* by Norman Joy — *Bees, Wasps,
Ants and Allied Insects of the British Isles* by Edward Step — *Bees
and Wasps* by O. H. Latter — *House Flies* by C. C. Hewitt — *The
Dragonflies of the British Isles* by Cynthia Longfield — *Insects,
their Structure and Life* by G. H. Carpenter.